Schroeder
Music Is My Life

SPARKLER BOOKS
AN IMPRINT OF PHAROS BOOKS • A SCRIPPS HOWARD COMPANY

Originally published and produced by
Arnoldo Mondadori Editore S.p.A., Milano

© 1988 United Feature Syndicate, Inc.
All rights reserved.
Based on the Italian Language Book
"Schroeder, una vita per la musica"
(© 1987 United Feature Syndicate, Inc.)
No part of this book may be reproduced in any form
or by any means without written permission
of the publisher.
LC 88-042736
ISBN 0-88687-376-2

Printed in Italy

Sparkler Books
An Imprint of Pharos Books
A Scripps Howard Company
200 Park Avenue
New York, NY 10166

10   9   8   7   6   5   4   3   2   1

CONTENTS

Schroeder loves music, especially Beethoven, and plays constantly on a toy piano. Usually reserved and busy practicing, Schroeder reacts only when Woodstock tries to make his piano a playground, or Lucy seeks to distract him by flirting. When Schroeder does leave the piano, it's to meet with his good friend Charlie Brown, whom he usually ends up defending from the rest of the gang. Occasionally he plays the catcher's position on the Peanuts baseball team, which can be fun. But best of all, Schroeder likes the piano and Beethoven, period.

Enough Already!

Can We Talk?

I'LL BET I KNOW SOMETHING YOU DON'T KNOW...

WHAT'S THAT?

BEETHOVEN NOW COMES IN SPRAY CANS!

Schroeder and Snoopy

Schroeder and Woodstock

Schroeder and the Rest of the Gang

© 1970 United Feature Syndicate, Inc.

33

Summer Music Camp

Pianoless

A Little Sweetness

43